11+ English Semantics

WORKBOOK 1

Synonyms

Stephen C. Curran

with Warren Vokes

Edited by

Andrea Richardson and Katrina MacKay

This book belongs to

Accelerated Education Publications Ltd.

eccentric hasty plentiful
admit inadvertent realize
success peace implicate

Exercise 1a

> Write the **synonym** for the word in **bold**.

1) There was a(n) **abundant** supply of food for everyone in the camp. _plentiful_

2) The climb was a great **accomplishment** in such adverse conditions. _____

3) In the showcase is the **actual** crown worn by King Henry VIII. _____

4) She tried to **accuse** her brother and make him share the blame. _____

5) He had to **abandon** the car and walk home in the snow. _____

6) He was very **able** at the crease and scored a century. _____

7) The **acrid** smell was coming through the laboratory's open door. _____

8) Although still a(n) **adolescent**, he was held responsible. _____

9) Their journey came to a(n) **abrupt** end when the car broke down. _____

10) The results are **achievable** with much hard work. _____ **Score** ⟋ 10

Exercise 1b

11) I **accept** that I was there but I'm not responsible. _____

12) The amount raised was **adequate** but less than they had expected. _____

13) After years of fighting, the warring factions finally reached **accord**. _____

14) They waited for the water flow to **abate** before launching the boat. _____

15) Three more were employed to **add to** the work force. _____

16) Once she had caught her breath, the **ache** in her side diminished. _____

17) His behaviour was **abnormal**, even for him! _____

18) I am ambitious and want to **accomplish** much in my life. _____

19) His reaction to the crisis was very **adult** for one so young. _____

20) The distraction caused the **accidental** foul. _____ **Score** ⟋ 10

2

pain
bitter
augment
juvenile

possible
genuine
satisfactory
mature

**Word Bank
TOTAL
20**

Across

1

1. Idiosyncratic
6. Allow
8. Discomfort
11. Insinuate
12. Triumph
14. Ceasefire
18. Involuntary
19. Enlarge
20. Ample

Down

2. Skilled
3. Viable
4. Sour
5. Fulfil
7. Acceptable
9. Older
10. Youthful
13. Diminish
15. Hurried
16. Real
17. Desert

Welcome to:
The Wonderful World of Synonyms.

A **Synonym** is a word that means the same, or almost the same, as another word, either in all of its uses or in a particular context.

Use the words shown at the top of each page once only in each question and each puzzle.

Put the mystery letter from the starred square (✳) into box **1** below. Add in the mystery letters from puzzles **2** to **8** then rearrange them to make **Oliver's Mystery Word**.

The clue is **MARINE LIFE**.

Enter your mystery letters here:

1	2	3	4	5	6	7	8

Now rearrange them to make the:

Mystery Word:

Score

/ 20

3

tough   **nimble**   **amenable**
accord   **open**   **federation**
budget   **height**   **wrath**
furious   **alive**   **disclose**

Across

2

1. Eager
4. Outraged
7. Sprightly
9. Settlement
11. Infuriate
12. Rage
13. Breathing
14. Gaping
16. Plan
17. Reveal
18. Pretty

Down

2. Placate
3. Open
5. Disinterested
6. Coalition
7. Irritation

8. Harsh
10. Detestable
11. Favourable
15. Elevation

Mystery Letter **Score**

20

Exercise 2a

1) She left the door **ajar** so she could hear if her baby cried. _____

2) The flies around his head whilst he is eating is a(n) **annoyance**. _____

3) He was **angry** with his friend when she lied to him. _____

4) His approach was **aggressive** and very frightening. _____

5) His mother tried to **appease** him when he lost his temper. _____

6) He tore **apart** the papers before putting them in the waste bin. _____

7) The companies formed a(n) **alliance** and agreed to work together. _____

8) They did not **announce** the winning candidate until after a recount. _____

9) Monkeys are very **agile** and swing from branch to branch with ease. _____

10) The dress was very **appealing**, so she bought it. _____   **Score** ___/ 10

Exercise 2b

11) The treasurer had to **allot** sufficient funds for the project. _____

12) The two parties reached an **agreement** which was acceptable to both. _____

13) Their day was ruined by the **appalling** weather. _____

14) He was **anxious** to set off early to avoid the heavy traffic. _____

15) "You're beginning to **annoy** me and test my patience!" _____

16) At 30,000 feet, the jet had reached its cruising **altitude**. _____

17) He was a very **agreeable** young man who never refused to help. _____

18) Linda is **apathetic** about every suggestion, no matter how exciting. _____

19) He lost his temper and made no attempt to hide his **anger**. _____

20) The fish on the surface was no longer **animate**. _____   **Score** ___/ 10

neat   **come**   **haughty**
attack   **guarantee**   **presence**
lucky   **verify**   **valid**

Across

3. Vacant
5. Permit
7. Gone
8. Approach
11. Orderly
12. Pretentious
14. Longing
16. Acceptable
17. Care
18. Substantiate
19. Existence

3

Down

1. Dispute
2. Raid
4. Go around
6. Fortunate
9. Assess
10. End
11. Discuss
13. Pledge
15. Steady

Mystery Letter   **Score**

20

6   © 2013 Stephen Curran

greed	circumvent
attention	out
stern	stabilize
empty	negotiate

Word Bank
TOTAL
60

Exercise 3a

1) His lack of **awareness** resulted in a serious accident. _____

2) They ended their long-running **argument** and became reconciled. _____

3) Your **attendance** is requested at the club's annual dinner. _____

4) Every room in the building was **bare** after the removal men departed. _____

5) She waited for her friend to **arrive** before ordering the meal. _____

6) The jeweller was asked to **authenticate** the diamond was real. _____

7) After her spending spree, she had to **appraise** her finances. _____

8) It is an **auspicious** start to the day and everything should go well. _____

9) His **avarice** was evident when he took more food than he could eat. _____

10) The rope at the **back** of the boat was not secured. _____ **Score** ☐ 10

Exercise 3b

11) He was a(*n*) **arrogant** individual full of his own self-importance. _____

12) The postman rang the doorbell but apparently they were **away**. _____

13) She tried to **bargain** with the stall holder but to no avail. _____

14) He needed his boss to **approve** the decision before proceeding. _____

15) The bedroom is very **arranged** with everything in its proper place. _____

16) It was a vicious **assault** against a fellow human being. _____

17) He struggled to **balance** the kayak in the turbulent water. _____

18) The satellite navigation system enabled him to **avoid** the jam. _____

19) They gave us every **assurance** it would arrive on time. _____ **Score**

20) The solicitor confirmed the document was **authorized**. _____ ☐ 10

cellar	pretty	early
importune	novice	dogma
advantage	partisan	offer
accused	noisy	merge

Across

4

5. Vault
7. Shambles
8. Proposal
12. Foothold
14. Tedious
15. View
16. Prematurely
17. Raucous
18. Handsome
19. Constraint
20. Learner

Down

1. Stoop
2. Chief
3. Peripheral
4. Fuse
6. Indicted
9. Dogmatic
10. Conceited
11. Clever
13. Solicit

Mystery Letter **Score**

20

vain
dull
limitation
intelligent
marginal
master
bend
disaster

Word Bank TOTAL 80

Exercise 4a

1) The scheme's main **benefit** is a guaranteed return on investment. ______________
2) He had arrived **beforehand** to be seated nearer the front. ______________
3) She **blamed** him and nothing he could say would change her mind. ______________
4) The research extended the **boundary** of their understanding. ______________
5) His subject knowledge was poor and the presentation was **boring**. ______________
6) Due to a lack of planning, it was a **calamity** waiting to happen. ______________
7) The **basement** was flooded after several days of heavy rain. ______________
8) The party's political **belief** was too radical for the electorate. ______________
9) He was **boastful** and brash and made few friends. ______________
10) She was only a **beginner** but she showed great promise. ______________

Score / **10**

Exercise 4b

11) It was sad to see her **beg** for money from passers-by. ______________
12) Their **boss** was a tyrant and worked the men far too hard. ______________
13) Their daughter was very **bright** and always top of the class. ______________
14) The decision was **borderline** and left the spectators bemused. ______________
15) She looked very **beautiful** without make up or expensive clothes. ______________
16) The **bid** was generous but insufficient to persuade them to sell. ______________
17) The force of the wind caused the tall conifer to **bow**. ______________
18) Disco music is **blaring** and can permanently damage your hearing. ______________
19) It is a very **biased** viewpoint that will alienate most people. ______________
20) The sky and sea seem to **blend** at the horizon. ______________

Score / **10**

caution	negligent	commemorate
memorial	internal	dare
hero	deceive	upbeat
gloomy	merry	paramount

Across

5

1. Dupe
3. Understandable
5. Wintry
8. Heart
11. Supreme
12. Idol
13. Jolly
15. Selection
16. Division
17. Sanitation
18. Monument

Down

2. Restraint
4. Respectful
5. Honour
6. Giggle
7. Dim
9. Remiss
10. Defy
11. Wholesome
14. Optimistic

Mystery Letter

Score

20

cold   **option**
laugh   **polite**
category   **pure**
hygiene   **lucid**

Exercise 5a

1) The complex **inner** workings of the machine often malfunction. _____

2) It is essential they proceed with **care** to avoid injury. _____

3) The scam was designed to confuse and **cheat** old people. _____

4) He had little **choice** than to carry on as if nothing had happened. _____

5) His instructions were **clear** and left little room for ambiguity. _____

6) The morning was bright and sunny and she felt extremely **cheerful**. _____

7) His **careless** behaviour was the cause of their demise. _____

8) She was not sure of the document's exact **classification**. _____

9) The character in the play was a **happy**, rotund individual. _____

10) Hospital **cleanliness** is vital to avoid infections. _____   **Score** 　/10

Exercise 5b

11) Every year the school has a service to **celebrate** founders' day. _____

12) The explorer was her **champion** who inspired her to succeed. _____

13) It was a **civil** question and he was surprised his friend took offence. _____

14) The **cenotaph** stands in the cemetery to honour fallen soldiers. _____

15) The dull weather cast a **cheerless** blanket over the countryside. _____

16) The clear, cold water in the mountain stream tasted **clean** and fresh. _____

17) He accepted the **challenge** to prove he was not afraid. _____

18) The **chief** reason for his visit was to meet his estranged sister. _____

19) She had to **chuckle** when she read the amusing article. _____

20) It was a bright but **chilly** day for a brisk walk. _____   **Score** 　/10

transparent	brilliant	ascend
rough	persuade	gather
giant	blend	banal
obedient	flatter	accept

Exercise 6a

1) "I **concur** with your findings and endorse your appraisal." _____

2) Far from being a rarity, the vase was **common** and worthless. _____

3) It is **compulsory** to drive on the left in the United Kingdom. _____

4) The material is too **coarse** to be worn against the skin. _____

5) It is usual to **confine** foreign nationals in times of war. _____

6) Speaking of her cooking, he could not **compliment** his wife enough. _____

7) Louis Pasteur was a **clever** French chemist and microbiologist. _____

8) Never challenging authority, he was a very **compliant** citizen. _____

9) He gave the court a **concise** version of the events he had witnessed. _____

10) Although tinted, the glass was still **clear**. _____   **Score** ◻/10

Exercise 6b

11) The kit should **comprise** needles, threads, thimble and buttons. _____

12) Robert Pershing Wadlow, the world's tallest man, was a **colossus**. _____

13) The envelope was addressed to his son and marked '**confidential**'. _____

14) Sir Edmund Hillary was the first man to **climb** Mount Everest. _____

15) He had to **comply** with the ruling and withdrew his complaint. _____

16) She tried to **coax** her son to do his homework. _____

17) At the **conclusion** of the party, every child left with a balloon. _____

18) He vowed to keep in touch with his **comrade** from the war. _____

19) **Combine** the ingredients to make a moist, rich, tasty cake. _____

20) He took his son to the woods to **collect** conkers. _____   **Score** ◻/10

Across

1. Required
3. Secret
5. Praise
10. Finale
11. Intern
12. Goliath
13. Acquaintance
16. Receive
17. Rise
18. Contain
19. Bristly

6

Down

2. Short
3. Encourage
4. Intelligent
6. Consent
7. Translucent
8. Mix
9. Amenable
14. Plain
15. Assemble

Mystery
Letter   Score

20

baffle
thrift
receptacle
limit

maze
regularly
perpetuate
manipulate

victory
obvious
negate
transfer

Across

7

2. Unsuspicious
5. Success
9. Refute
11. Investor
14. Restrain
16. Prudence
18. Dear
19. Shape
20. Resolve

Down

1. Preserve
3. Deceive
4. Definite
6. Systematically
7. Repository
8. Muddle

10. Yearning
12. Exact
13. Mimic
15. Move
17. Disapprove

Mystery
Letter   Score

20

14

© 2013 Stephen Curran

Word Bank TOTAL 140

Exercise 7a

1) We should **curb** our vehicle speed in built-up areas. _____

2) She was keen to **correct** her mistake and repair the damage. _____

3) Success was achieved by implementing a policy of **conservation**. _____

4) It is not reasonable to **criticize** others if you, too, are at fault. _____

5) It was **correct** to assume the house was empty when the fire started. _____

6) It is important not to **confuse** the audience with scientific facts. _____

7) Listen! That macaw is trying to **copy** the telephone's ring. _____

8) Her **craving** for chocolate intensified during her pregnancy. _____

9) There is a(n) **conspicuous** absence of members attending the meeting. _____

10) I wish to **convey** the property to my brother. _____   Score ☐ / 10

Exercise 7b

11) The document is a complete **confusion** of rules and regulations. _____

12) Please put your empty bottles and cans in the **container** provided. _____

13) His younger brother is extremely **credulous** and very easily led. _____

14) The final **conquest** was achieved at a high cost in human lives. _____

15) Their **costly** mistake would have serious financial implications. _____

16) He always tries to **influence** my opinion by saying I'm naïve. _____

17) Her bad behaviour **consistently** interrupted the lessons. _____

18) The bank was the company's main **creditor** and had to be repaid. _____

19) This new evidence may **contradict** our previous findings. _____   Score

20) "Shall we **continue** this discussion after the lesson?" _____   ☐ / 10

guile
term
bold

guardian
harmful
night

habitual
smart
bright

Exercise 8a

1) The humid conditions caused the dead leaves to **decompose** rapidly. _____

2) It is **crucial** to maintain excellent hygiene standards in hospitals. _____

3) Her dress hung loosely, accentuating her **delicate** frame. _____

4) Her **custodian** took care of her while she was underage. _____

5) The rumours are very **damaging** and he is keen to repudiate them. _____

6) The umpire **allowed** their appeal and declared the batsman out. _____

7) The rock sample proved to be a very **dense** material. _____

8) Just being present at the scene of the crime made him **culpable**. _____

9) The contract had run its full **cycle** and needed renewing. _____

10) The rocket exploded in a **dazzling** profusion of colours. _____

Score

/10

Exercise 8b

11) Finishing schools produced highly **cultured** young ladies. _____

12) He lied about his past in a(n) **deliberate** attempt to confuse them. _____

13) It was a **daring** plan that would rely on stealth and total surprise. _____

14) They were **delighted** to see their mother looking so happy. _____

15) The accounts highlighted a huge **deficit** in the company's finances. _____

16) He used all his **cunning** to confuse the enemy and avoid capture. _____

17) As **darkness** fell, the temperature dropped to below freezing. _____

18) A bowl of porridge and a cup of coffee are his **customary** breakfast. _____

19) He looked very **dapper** in his new school uniform. _____

Score

20) She was quite **definite**: no smoking allowed indoors. _____

/10

Word Bank TOTAL 160

Across

8

3. Deceit
6. Refined
7. Responsible
10. Shortfall
11. Blocked
14. Toxic
15. Duration
16. Dwindle
17. Dusk
18. Planned

Down

1. Agreed
2. Slender
4. Specific
5. Elegant
7. Pleased
8. Vital
9. Fearless
12. Carer
13. Vivid
14. Regular

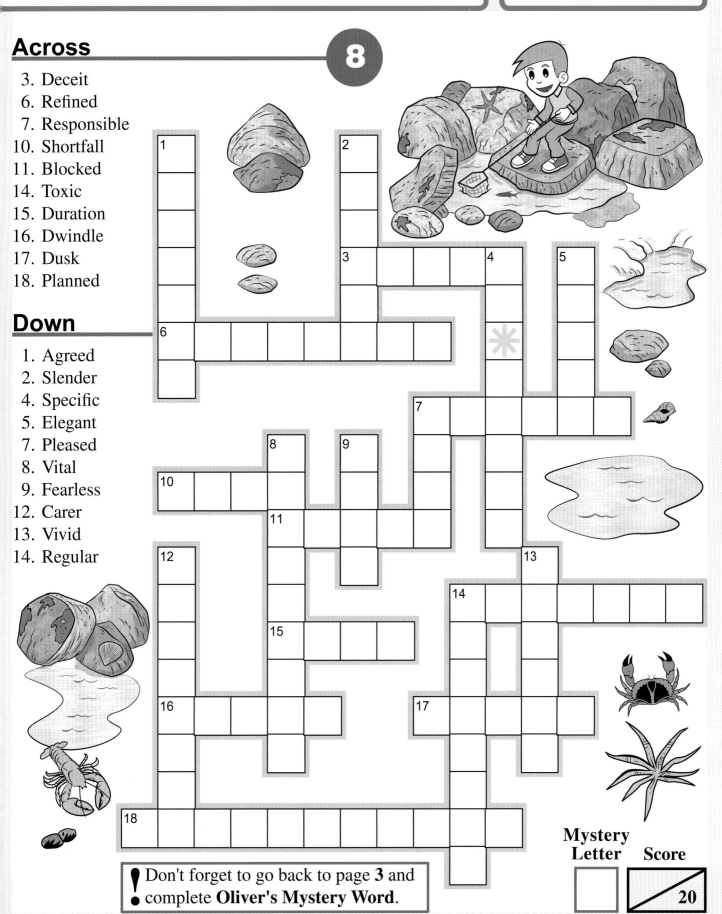

Don't forget to go back to page **3** and complete **Oliver's Mystery Word**.

Mystery Letter

Score

/20

conceive	craving	cease
barren	isolate	captivity
hate	adversity	lead

Exercise 9a

1) Could you, just for once, **detach** yourself from your video game? ＿＿＿＿＿＿

2) You cannot **deny** it: the evidence is very clear! ＿＿＿＿＿＿

3) I think you'll **discover** that all the chocolates have been eaten. ＿＿＿＿＿＿

4) He was tired, cold and hungry and had never felt so **dispirited**. ＿＿＿＿＿＿

5) I **detest** all kinds of violence and the bullies that revel in it. ＿＿＿＿＿＿

6) He is very **dependable** and willing to undertake almost any task. ＿＿＿＿＿＿

7) Will you please **desist** from playing your music so loudly! ＿＿＿＿＿＿

8) I persuaded her to **discard** the candle and use her torch. ＿＿＿＿＿＿

9) Please **direct** me to Mr. Neville, with whom I have an appointment. ＿＿＿＿＿＿

10) The whole plan was **disordered** and inefficient. ＿＿＿＿＿＿ **Score** ⬛ 10

Exercise 9b

11) It is only a matter of time before motor cars **deplete** the oil reserves. ＿＿＿＿＿＿

12) She does not allow her **disability** to impede her progress. ＿＿＿＿＿＿

13) The **dirt** on his shirt was a indication of his poor work environment. ＿＿＿＿＿＿

14) It is imperative that we **design** a better way to recycle plastic. ＿＿＿＿＿＿

15) He was arrested and placed in **detention** while his fate was decided. ＿＿＿＿＿＿

16) They crested the hill only to see a **desolate** landscape beyond. ＿＿＿＿＿＿

17) The highly infectious **disease** was fast becoming a pandemic. ＿＿＿＿＿＿

18) He nurtured a strong **desire** to succeed where others had failed. ＿＿＿＿＿＿

19) He looked down in a(n) **disdainful** manner on those less fortunate. ＿＿＿＿＿＿

20) He overcame every **difficulty** to achieve his goal. ＿＿＿＿＿＿ **Score** ⬛ 10

Across

9

1. Imprisonment
3. Lifeless
6. Imperious
7. Empty
10. Create
12. Precede
16. Misfortune
17. Loathe
18. Squalor

Down

1. Oppose
2. Sterile
4. Longing
5. Unearth
8. Weakness
9. Trustworthy
10. Stop
11. Messy
13. Dump
14. Sickness
15. Quarantine

Put the mystery letters from the starred squares (✳) from puzzles **9** to **15** into their numbered box below, then rearrange them to make **Kate's Mystery Word**. The clue is **HOSPITAL**.

Enter your mystery letters:

9	10	11	12	13	14	15

Now rearrange them to make the:

Mystery Word:

Score

/20

nature   discourage   clear

eminent   anguish   section

tame   contribution   entrance

fall   blunt   mute

Across

10

2. Friendly
4. Discounted
6. Character
8. Luxury
11. Falseness
13. Plunge
17. Speechless
18. Grant
19. Zealous
20. Prominent

Down

1. Portion
3. Acute
5. Treachery
7. Home
9. Opening
10. Oppose
12. Sharp
14. Sorrow
15. Unsharpened
16. Terrain

Mystery Letter   **Score**

20

hypocrisy   **betrayal**
abode   **keen**
eager   **land**
comfort   **cheap**

Word Bank
TOTAL
200

Exercise 10a

1) An anonymous benefactor made a huge **donation** to the charity. _____

2) Bulk buying usually proves to be a very **economical** alternative. _____

3) Going behind his back was a **disloyalty** she found hard to bear. _____

4) His untimely death was the cause of much **distress** to his family. _____

5) Her compassionate **disposition** touched everyone who knew her. _____

6) The **earth** was churned up by the heavy equipment. _____

7) The feral cats were cared for and eventually became **domesticated**. _____

8) The surprise rendered her **dumb** until she regained her composure. _____

9) After many stressful years at work, he retired to lead a life of **ease**. _____

10) He tried to **dissuade** her from turning back. _____   **Score** ⬛/10

Exercise 10b

11) Their **dwelling** was basic but they welcomed a roof over their heads. _____

12) The sales **division** of the company was relocating to Birmingham. _____

13) It was sad to witness such **duplicity** from one so well-principled. _____

14) He was very **excited** and urged everyone to come with him. _____

15) There is a very **distinct** smell of petrol in this car. _____

16) **Intense** competition required them to perform at their very best. _____

17) The **doorway** opened into a vast room with a magnificent ceiling. _____

18) He was a very **distinguished** scientist and Nobel prize winner. _____

19) They watched the stricken helicopter **drop** from the sky. _____

20) His razor was **dull** and made shaving difficult. _____   **Score** ⬛/10

radiate	exhilarated	qualified
elaborate	illustrious	fatigue
vacant	permanent	like
wax	great	build

Exercise 11a

1) The full extent of his injuries were not immediately **evident**. _____

2) Their first priority was to **erect** a shelter to protect themselves. _____

3) Next, it was **essential** to find a supply of potable water. _____

4) This **evil** act is clearly the work of terrorists. _____

5) If you **exclude** them from the guest list they will be very offended. _____

6) Her smile would **effuse** happiness and joy to everyone present. _____

7) The office building had stood **empty** for over six years. _____

8) It is difficult to **estimate** the distance in the fading light. _____

9) On completing her training, she was a **certified** engineer. _____ **Score**

10) The Shard is a(n) **enormous** architectural achievement. _____ /10

Exercise 11b

11) He was **elated** by the news of his father's recovery from illness. _____

12) Her supervisor is very **exacting** and expects far too much from her. _____

13) With the onset of senility, names and dates began to **escape** him. _____

14) 18 miles into the marathon, she was overcome with **exhaustion**. _____

15) I **esteem** the beauty of the portrait and the skill of the artist. _____

16) Torvill and Dean formed a(n) **enduring** ice-skating partnership. _____

17) The moon's own shadow causes it appear to **enlarge** and decrease. _____

18) Her mother knew she would **enjoy** the surprise she had planned. _____

19) She is an **eminent** member of parliament. _____ **Score**

20) He would **embellish** the story each time he told it. _____ /10

22   © 2013 Stephen Curran ae

elude	**necessary**
cherish	**judge**
visible	**bad**
fastidious	**omit**

Word Bank TOTAL 220

11

Across

3. Emanate
6. Enhance
9. Remove
12. Noticeable
13. Weariness
15. Unending
16. Love
18. Certified

Down

1. Expand
2. Free
4. Particular
5. Awful
7. Zestful
8. Construct
10. Famous
11. Immense
14. Needed
17. Referee
19. Adore
20. Avoid

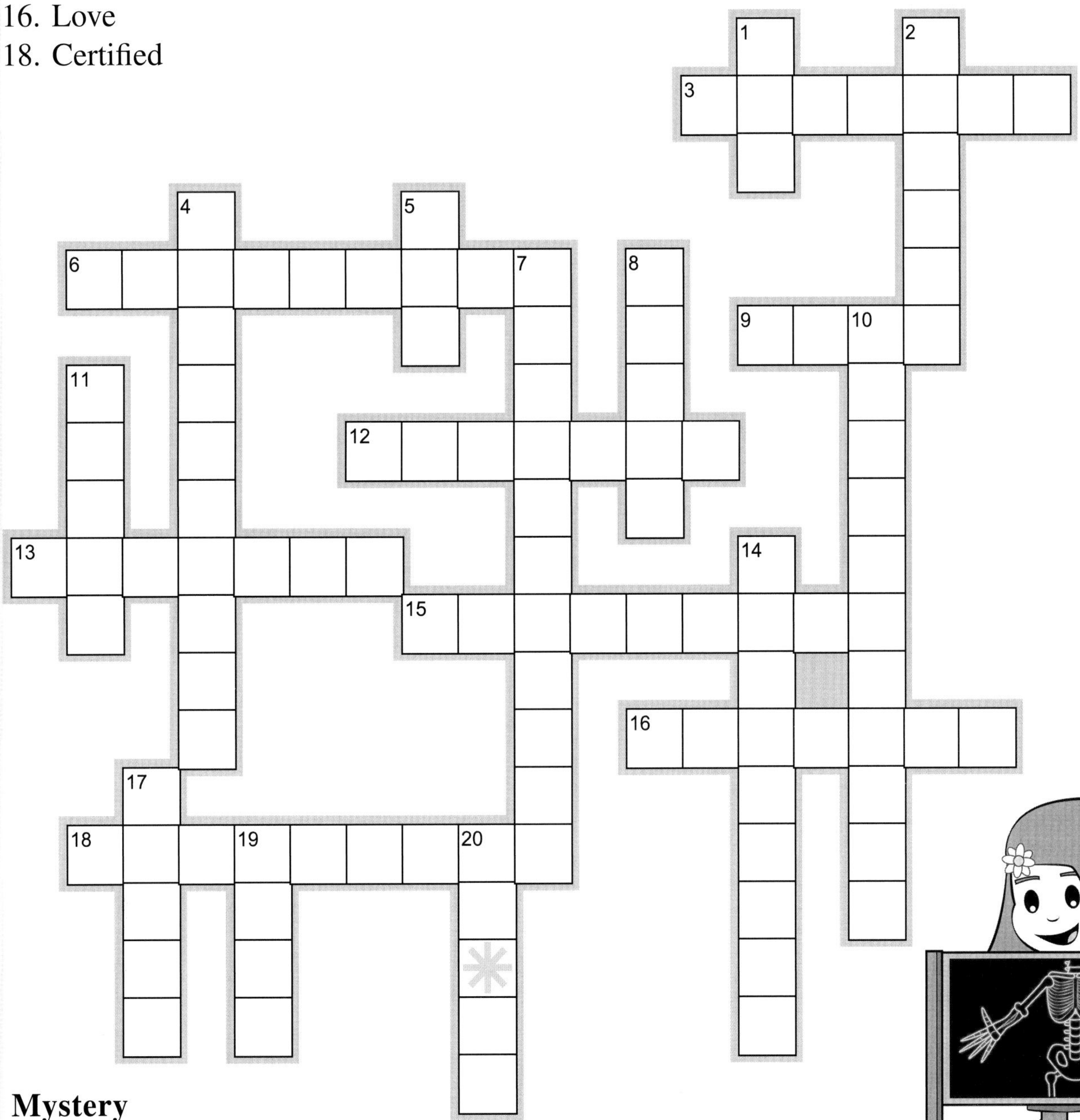

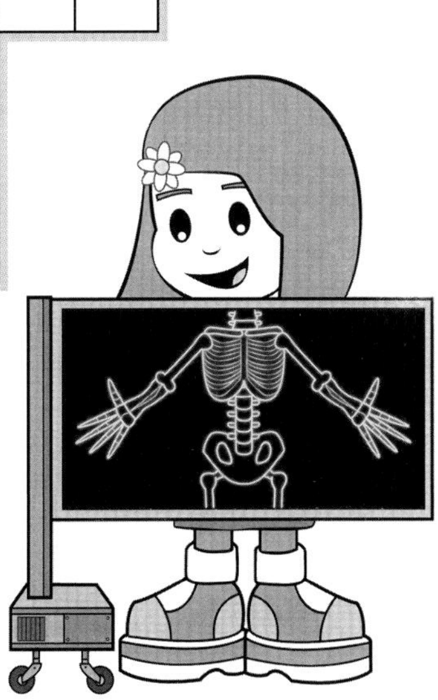

Mystery Letter

Score /20

justification long bonus
myth truth justice
loyal imitation brisk
parent grope rank

Across

12

Down

2. Paramount
4. Pungent
5. Reason
9. Ultimate
10. Lengthy
14. Assured
16. Steadfast
17. Mother
18. Solid
19. Clear

1. Righteousness
2. Addition
3. Veracity

6. Artificial
7. Auspicious
8. Fumble
11. Swift
12. Complete
13. Vigorous
15. Legend

Mystery Letter **Score**

20

full	last	Word Bank
sunny	best	TOTAL
hard	healthy	240
opportune	definite	

Exercise 12a

1) It was a(n) **fitting** occasion on which to announce her retirement. _____

2) The low price at which it was offered seemed to prove it was a(n) **fake**. _____

3) Their nostrils were filled with the **fetid** odour of rotting meat. _____

4) At times it seems **fairness** is overlooked in the interests of equality. _____

5) She gently squeezed the plums to see if they were too **firm** to eat. _____

6) It was the **final** leg of their journey and they would soon be home. _____

7) There was no **fixed** date by which the project had to be completed. _____

8) He had to **feel** around for his keys that had fallen under the car seat. _____

9) Such a **fine** and warm day suggested spring was not too far away. _____

10) They set a **fast** pace to reach home before dusk. _____   **Score** ⟋ 10

Exercise 12b

11) Regular exercise keeps you **fit** in both mind and body. _____

12) The water butt was **filled** to the brim by the heavy rain shower. _____

13) She chose the **finest** dress from her wardrobe to wear at the party. _____

14) Her **father** drove her to the station to catch the earlier train. _____

15) There is no **excuse** for your behaviour: you should know better! _____

16) A jury should only concern itself with matters of **fact**. _____

17) He worked very late and was due a(n) **extra** payment. _____

18) They took a(n) **extended** holiday to visit their son in New Zealand. _____

19) His version of events turned out to be a complete **fable**. _____

20) His **faithful** dog died and he was inconsolable. _____   **Score** ⟋ 10

horizontal	enemy	prohibit
ancestor	always	frank
feeble	common	dense
mad	inhale	assemble

Exercise 13a

1) Her **graceless** performance was almost too embarrassing to watch. _____

2) The rules of the game strictly **forbid** the use of a dictionary. _____

3) He looks like a savage with his **full** head of hair and bushy beard. _____

4) The decree ordered everyone should **gather** in the town square. _____

5) In the **gloom**, I could just make out the shape of the building. _____

6) He was very **forthright** during their discussion and upset his wife. _____

7) They lifted the stretcher slowly, to keep the patient **flat** and secure. _____

8) She felt someone **grab** her arm and pull her towards them. _____

9) If you wish to **gratify** me, do as you're told and sit down. _____ **Score**

10) Her **forebear** fought at Balaclava in the Crimean War. _____

	10

Exercise 13b

11) He is a very **genial** man and a pleasure to be around. _____

12) The illness left her very **frail** and had aged her terribly. _____

13) Their **foe** were well dug in and an attack in daylight would be folly. _____

14) We woke to a **gorgeous** summer morning and set off for the beach. _____

15) **Frequent** visitors to Britain, swallows winter in southern Africa. _____

16) The sun was low and its **gleam** was blinding him as he drove into it. _____

17) Her continual complaining makes me so **furious**. _____

18) He will be remembered **forever** as a man of principle and honour. _____

19) He was winded and could only **gasp** noisily and spasmodically. _____

20) Cats are **graceful** in appearance and movement. _____ **Score**

	10

jovial
dark
grasp
awkward

glare
beautiful
dainty
please

Across

1. Breathe
4. Packed
5. Blackness
7. Glisten
10. Inept
11. Permanently
12. Delight
15. Widespread
17. Rival
18. Picturesque
19. Veto

13

Down

2. Accumulate
3. Level
6. Blunt
7. Hold
8. Irate
9. Delicate
13. Predecessor
14. Merry
16. Meagre

Mystery Letter   **Score**

/20

sorrow   **lament**   **increase**
estimate   **credulous**   **hinder**
bliss   **poverty**   **lofty**
aid   **top**   **past**

Across

3. Escalation
6. Privation
7. Pure
12. Assist
13. Joy
14. Approximation
17. Keep
18. Mourn
20. Trusting

14

Down

1. Aperture
2. Erect
4. Truthful
5. Sadness
8. Saver
9. Antiquity
10. Impede

11. Shame
15. Aloof
16. Mammoth
19. Uppermost

Mystery Letter

Score

20

miser	detain
gap	candid
decent	straight
immense	humiliate

Exercise 14a

1) He used the spirit level to check the shelf was perfectly **horizontal**. _____

2) Their **grief** was eased by the knowledge that his suffering had ended. _____

3) Many of the world's inhabitants live in conditions of **hardship**. _____

4) The **highest** branches were at least fifty feet from the ground. _____

5) She taunted her sister, in front of her friends, to **humble** her. _____

6) Our nation's **history** is riddled with wars, battles and other conflicts. _____

7) A **guess** at the result helps to verify the correct solution. _____

8) A(n) **huge** silo contained 250,000 bushels of wheat. _____

9) The passers-by rushed to **help** the old lady when she fell. _____

10) He was a(n) **honourable** man with traditional values. _____

Score

/ 10

Exercise 14b

11) He was well known as a **hoarder** who loathed to spend money. _____

12) To **grieve** the loss of a loved one is an overwhelming emotion. _____

13) The bad weather would **hamper** their attempts to reach the victim. _____

14) Her feeling of superiority was evident from her **haughty** manner. _____

15) His lawyer argued that the police could **hold** him no longer. _____

16) It was her **honest** opinion and she would not be dissuaded. _____

17) The **growth** in the world's population continues at an alarming rate. _____

18) Their **happiness** was cut short by bad news from home. _____

19) His vulnerability was a result of being young and **naïve**. _____

20) The **hole** under the fence had become bigger overnight. _____

Score

/ 10

Exercise 15a

1) His **initial** reaction was panic but he knew he had to take control. _____

2) His explanation was **inconsistent** and not taken seriously. _____

3) She gave a(n) **impromptu** speech that captivated the audience. _____

4) **Inside** the city walls the inhabitants were safe from attack. _____

5) His **inconsequential** attempt to change events was just a ruse. _____

6) The carcasses were **hung** on butchers' hooks from the rails above. _____

7) It was a(n) **innocuous** gesture but it antagonized his opponent. _____

8) The lorry remained **inactive**, awaiting repair in the workshop. _____

9) It was mufti day at the office so her clothes were **informal**. _____

10) She's an **idealist** who is never downhearted. _____ Score ◻ 10

Exercise 15b

11) She has a(n) **inclination** to giggle whenever she is embarrassed. _____

12) The new substance is totally **inflexible** and has immense strength. _____

13) The closed circuit television caught her **napping** while on duty. _____

14) They are **identical** and together make a valuable matching pair. _____

15) He tried to **dodge** the cricket ball but it struck him on the chest. _____

16) He remained **inert** on the ground whilst the paramedics treated him. _____

17) It is a very **important** problem that needs to be resolved quickly. _____

18) The **inner** room has less natural light and is smaller than the rest. _____

19) He is a(n) **indolent** individual who expects others to wait on him. _____

20) The **imitation** flowers look surprisingly realistic. _____ Score ◻ 10

passive	rigid
casual	first
interior	harmless
asleep	within

Word Bank TOTAL 300

Across

4. Mild
6. Visionary
8. Slumbering
11. Unresponsive
12. Pretend
16. Similar
17. Significant
19. Unfounded
20. Unoccupied

Down

1. Earliest
2. Dangling
3. Trivial
5. Inside
7. Shun
9. Instinctive
10. Occasional
13. Trend
14. Lethargic
15. Indoors
18. Stiff

! Don't forget to go back to page **19** and
• complete **Kate's Mystery Word**.

Mystery Letter

Score / 20

virtue	fervour	inside
tangle	happy	generous
hill	absence	settle

Exercise 16a

1) She approached her work with a rare emotional **intensity**. _____

2) The aim of the homily was to **laud** the deceased and his good works. _____

3) The birth of their son was a **joyful** event that completed their family. _____

4) "I **insist** you join us and I won't take no for an answer!" _____

5) His actions are not **legal** and, before long, will land him in trouble. _____

6) This medication will **lessen** the pain and help you sleep. _____

7) She took a **lenient** approach to the offence and only issued a caution. _____

8) The numbers are too **insufficient** to enable the trip to go ahead. _____

9) The bluetit tried to **land** on the feeder to peck at the fat ball. _____

10) The harsh exercise regime left him **lean** and fit. _____   Score ⬚ 10

Exercise 16b

11) He used the fine example set by his favourite athlete to **inspire** him. _____

12) He is a wonderfully **kind** man who has helped many charities. _____

13) She was not sure she could **last** another day without food and water. _____

14) Whilst he was a prisoner, the loss of his **liberty** was hard to bear. _____

15) He is a man of high **integrity** and cannot be corrupted. _____

16) They concluded that the driver's **lack** of sleep caused the accident. _____

17) The **internal** dimensions indicate the room has the required space. _____

18) A **large** cauldron of boiling water hung from a tripod over the fire. _____

19) Stuffing the cables into the box causes them to **intertwine**. _____

20) He used the small **knoll** to fix a compass bearing. _____   Score ⬚ 10

big
bless
lawful
decrease

endure
slim
liberal
freedom

Word Bank
TOTAL
320

Across

16

2. Indoor
4. Embolden
7. Sanction
8. Delighted
10. Scarce
11. Passion
13. Twist
16. Slender
18. Persist
19. Independence
20. Deficiency

Down

1. Vast
3. Subside
5. Giving
6. Permitted
9. Perch
12. Morality
14. Peak
15. Open-minded
17. Order

Put the mystery letters (✳) from puzzles **16** to **23** into their numbered box below then rearrange them to make **Dickens's Mystery Word**.
The clue is **COMPUTERS**.

Enter your mystery letters here:

16	17	18	19	20	21	22	23

Now rearrange them to make the:

Mystery Word:

Score / 20

alleviate   **tall**   **nice**
affectionate   **fortunate**   **noble**
cruel   **approach**   **courage**
powerful   **gentle**   **caricature**

Across

17

2. Meek
5. Demonstrative
8. Towering
11. Misjudge
13. Dreary
14. Advance
18. Pleasant
19. Auspicious
20. Mitigate

Down

1. Nature
3. Sovereign
4. Desolate
6. Impersonate
7. Forceful
9. Anguish
10. Wet
12. Distinguished
15. Pluck
16. Tender
17. Spiteful

Mystery Letter   **Score**

20

wretched	dismal
despair	misunderstand
humble	damp
king	temper

Exercise 17a

1) He knelt before his **monarch** to receive his knighthood. _____

2) It is a **modest** house but sufficient for their current needs. _____

3) Neglect had left the animal in a **miserable** condition. _____

4) The jailer is **merciless** and treats his prisoners with contempt. _____

5) The new puppy may **lighten** her sense of loss of her faithful dog. _____

6) His sudden **mood** changes make him a very difficult person. _____

7) He was in a state of abject **misery** and could not be consoled. _____

8) The underwater earthquake caused a **mighty** tsunami to rush inland. _____

9) It was a **lovely**, hot, sunny day: perfect for spending on the beach. _____

10) The heavy dew made the grass cold and **moist**. _____ Score ◻ / 10

Exercise 17b

11) It was easy to **misread** the situation and not appreciate the danger. _____

12) The winning dog has a **magnificent** face and a character to match. _____

13) The driving conditions were made worse by the **murky** weather. _____

14) "It will test their **mettle** and separate the men from the boys!" _____

15) She was blessed with a **mild** manner that comforted her patients. _____

16) The **lofty** trees cast long shadows across the field. _____

17) It was **lucky** you were passing by just when I needed you. _____

18) It was a tried and tested **method** that usually brought success. _____

19) Her **loving** husband never left for work without a kiss. _____ Score

20) His actions were intended to **mimic** their shortcomings. _____ ◻ / 10

strong	perplex	home
close	excited	impartial
near	fleet	loud
fail	lawyer	significant

Exercise 18a

1) Over-eating and lack of exercise made him **obese** and unhealthy. _____

2) There was not much **opportunity** for improvement in the results. _____

3) "**Shut** the door behind you when you go into the aviary." _____

4) His **muscular** frame made him an ideal choice for the front row. _____

5) The **notary** drew up the papers she needed to complete the deal. _____

6) Her movement was **nimble** and she covered the ground effortlessly. _____

7) Her **opposition** to the proposal was overruled by the council. _____

8) Complex chemical formulae never fail to **mystify** me. _____

9) It was a **novel**, yet simple, solution to an old problem. _____

10) The trees' foliage returned with the **onset** of spring. _____

Score

/10

Exercise 18b

11) Her fidgeting and endless chatter shows how **nervous** she is. _____

12) Failure to **notice** the change in the conditions left them vulnerable. _____

13) It was impossible to be heard beside the **noisy** machinery. _____

14) The **old** inscriptions proved that civilization had once existed here. _____

15) The country celebrated when the **national** team won the world cup. _____

16) Overloading the vehicle caused the rear suspension to **collapse**. _____

17) The judge always has to remain **neutral** throughout the trial. _____

18) He could be **obstinate** at times and refuse all assistance. _____

19) The time is **nigh** to view the long-awaited eclipse. _____

Score

20) His **noteworthy** performance ensured their success. _____

/10

Across

2. Miscarry
4. Close
6. Fasten
8. Appearance
9. Watch
10. Important
11. Baffle
14. Powerful
16. Fair
17. Domestic

18

Down

1. Solicitor
3. Stubborn
4. Original
5. Protest
7. Swift
8. Prehistoric
12. Anxious
13. Deafening
14. Latitude
15. Stout

Mystery Letter

Score

20

exterior   **forget**   **dry**
ally   **tranquil**   **queer**
sense   **shrewd**   **ideal**

Across

19

1. Occupied
3. Presenter
4. Think
7. Guide
10. Corrugate
11. Serene
14. Cunning
17. Odd
19. External
20. Feel

Down

2. Ample
5. Friend
6. Best
8. Rich
9. Dehydrated
12. Commotion
13. Civil
15. Surgeon
16. Arctic
18. Neglect

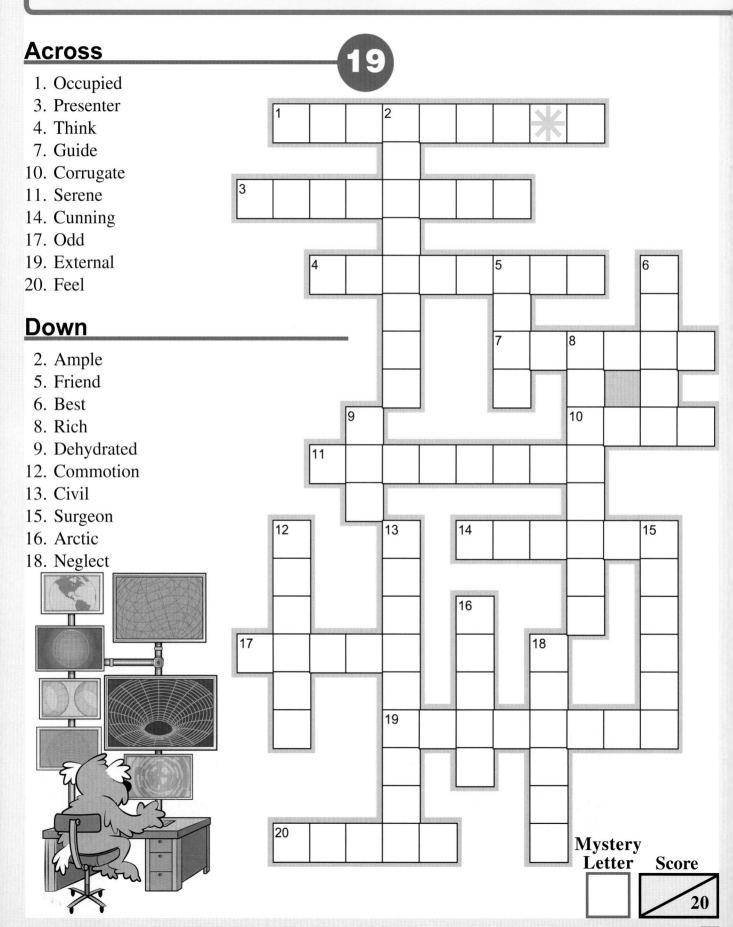

Mystery Letter

Score

20

doctor   fold
affluent   abundant
North   courteous
meditate   inhabited

Exercise 19a

1) She pressed the **pleat** in her skirt after she had washed it. _____

2) The thief made his escape in the **uproar** that followed. _____

3) The **organizer** and his group set off on their African safari. _____

4) Inuits **populated** the coastal regions of the Canadian Arctic. _____

5) He is very **perceptive** and not easily fooled. _____

6) The caterer served a(n) **plentiful** supply of dishes for the buffet. _____

7) It has not rained for weeks and the land is **parched**. _____

8) They found a **peaceful** location for their picnic beside the lake. _____

9) She was left to **deliberate** on the situation and suggest a way forward. _____

10) It's easy to **overlook** the needs of others. _____   Score ☐ /10

Exercise 19b

11) A very **peculiar** vehicle, with six wheels and no doors, drew up. _____

12) Their many layers of clothing made it difficult to **perceive** the cold. _____

13) When complaining, being **polite** usually leads to a better resolution. _____

14) The **polar** region is a freezing, inhospitable place for humans. _____

15) She searched in vain to find the **perfect** gift for her friend. _____

16) She appreciated the support given to her by her **partner**. _____

17) He is a fine **orator**: very knowledgeable and interesting to hear. _____

18) She applied for entry into medical school to train as a **physician**. _____

19) His successful businesses made him very **prosperous**. _____

20) The **outside** walls needed repointing. _____   Score ☐ /10

puny	approval	bias
omen	here	likely
advance	deep	sow
correct	landlord	goad

Exercise 20a

1) A period of unsettled weather is **probable** for the next few days. _____

2) It was easy to **purloin** the ring while the jeweller's back was turned. _____

3) She hoped she would receive a **quick** reply to her email. _____

4) He waited for **ratification** of the result before celebrating. _____

5) His **prejudice** was obvious from the comments he made. _____

6) These rumours will only **propagate** anxiety among the staff. _____

7) Years of disease and ill health had taken its toll and left him **frail**. _____

8) He wrote to the **proprietor** about the increased rent charges. _____

9) Everyone is **present** for the first night of the show. _____

10) The river's **rapid** stream tore the boat from its moorings. _____

Score

/ 10

Exercise 20b

11) Always be sure you have the **proper** equipment before setting off. _____

12) She had a **profound** belief in the spirit world and ghosts. _____

13) In hindsight, the events could be seen as an obvious **premonition**. _____

14) She sought **praise** from her parents for her achievement in the exam. _____

15) The sergeant ordered his platoon to **proceed** at walking pace. _____

16) It may be unwise to **provoke** your adversary before a contest. _____

17) With one last, desperate **push**, he managed to force open the door. _____

18) His ambition to **purchase** a new car every two years was thwarted. _____

19) "Be **prudent** and keep some cash in reserve." _____

20) She displayed much **prudence** in resolving the problem. _____

Score

/ 10

40

© 2013 Stephen Curran

wisdom
buy
thrust
fast

frugal
embezzle
prompt
confirmation

Across

20

4. Hasty
6. Authorization
7. Plant
9. Standard
11. Proof
12. Near
14. Sign
15. Procure
18. Expected
19. Prepayment

Down

1. Fleet
2. Badger
3. Owner
4. Scrawny
5. Shove
8. Rationality
10. Steal
13. Thrifty
16. Predisposition
17. Bottomless

Mystery Letter   **Score**

20

regret	take	famous
answer	pause	shopkeeper
withdraw	backward	reconcile

Across

2. Spherical
3. Repentance
5. Solution
7. Recovered
8. Rearward
10. Seize
11. Wander
15. Recurrent
16. Impudent
17. Hesitate
18. Retreat
19. Seafarer

21

Down

1. Accelerate
4. Resilient
6. Refuge
9. Vendor
12. Control
13. Diminish
14. Reunite
15. Celebrated

Mystery
Letter   Score

/20

ramble	durable
circular	insolent
manage	hasten
security	mariner

Word Bank TOTAL 420

Exercise 21a

1) She left the room and, eventually, she **regained** her composure. _____

2) She rang the number several times but there was no **response**. _____

3) The tide would have to **recede** before they could sit on the beach. _____

4) He showed no **remorse** when he appeared before the court. _____

5) After a short **rest**, while the reel was changed, the film continued. _____

6) He is a world **renowned** actor who has appeared in many films. _____

7) The trains are very **regular** so there is no need to rush. _____

8) She tried to **remove** the clock without him noticing. _____

9) He would **roam** around the streets aimlessly, trying to clear his mind. _____

10) Like his father before him, he was a **sailor** too. _____   Score ⬚/10

Exercise 21b

11) The **retailer** found it difficult to compete with the supermarkets. _____

12) He tried to **rush** her decision by applying unnecessary pressure. _____

13) It was a **round** turret designed to sweep through 360 degrees. _____

14) His injury forced him to **retire** from the competition. _____

15) He tried to **run** his uncle's business but was found wanting. _____

16) The sea defences are **robust** in both design and construction. _____

17) Air travel took a **retrograde** step when Concorde was grounded. _____

18) "I have never taught such a(n) **rude** child!" _____

19) His crew's **safety** was their captain's prime consideration. _____   Score

20) It was impossible to **reunite** the adopted children. _____   ⬚/10

permeate	economize	meagre
conceal	prudent	reconciliation
acute	export	reveal
disease	foolish	honest

Exercise 22a

1) She was laid low by the **sickness** she contracted whilst on holiday. _____

2) The magician was not prepared to **show** the trick's secret. _____

3) The **sensible** option was to surrender before they were massacred. _____

4) She was a **smart** candidate with an aptitude for figures. _____

5) The robbers planned to **split** their haul equally between themselves. _____

6) The bump had left a **slight** dent in the rear door. _____

7) A small hole allowed the rain to **saturate** the shed's contents. _____

8) The **spiral** motion left them feeling dizzy and nauseous. _____

9) The company had to **ship** the goods to Egypt. _____

10) Her **slim** body was able to squeeze through the gap. _____

Score

/ 10

Exercise 22b

11) He switched supplier to **save** on the cost of gas and electricity. _____

12) A **smaller** group formed to oppose the resolution but lost the vote. _____

13) She felt a(n) **sharp** pain in her back as she turned awkwardly. _____

14) The animal's **smooth** coat showed it was in excellent condition. _____

15) It was a **silly** mistake he was to regret for the rest of his life. _____

16) Although a **sly** way to win, he had no qualms about his deception. _____

17) He had enough time to **secrete** the map before he was apprehended. _____

18) His apology was **sincere** and was accepted by the committee. _____

19) They reached a **settlement** that satisfied both parties. _____

20) Only a **scanty** amount of food remained in store. _____

Score

/ 10

Across

22

3. Thin
6. Knowledgeable
8. Expose
11. Compromise
14. Cut down
17. Lesser
18. Discreet
19. Minute

Down

1. Paltry
2. Glossy
4. Ailment
5. Invade
6. Circular
7. Apportion

9. Truthful
10. Keen
12. Irrational
13. Camouflage
15. Wily
16. Distribute

Mystery
Letter   **Score**

/ 20

Across   **23**   ## Down

5. Arrest
6. Distribute
9. Squat
10. Viscous
11. Fasten
12. Abnormal
14. Mediocre
15. Improved
16. Grimly
17. Declare
18. Amazing

1. Severe
2. Correspond
3. Trivial
4. Introduction
7. Lesser
8. Fascinating
9. Sizable
10. Blustery
13. Soiled

Mystery Letter

Score 20

! Don't forget to go back to page **33** and complete **Dickens's Mystery Word**.

junior inferior
large dirty
shallow better
astonishing match

Exercise 23a

1) He is very ruthless and presides over a very **strict** regime. _____

2) The **start** of the race is scheduled for tomorrow morning. _____

3) The company accepts the work is **substandard** and will rectify it. _____

4) He read the instructions to see which parts he should **stick** together. _____

5) The forecaster predicts a wet, **stormy** night with gale-force winds. _____

6) He failed to **state** he not gained enough support for the project. _____

7) He trusted his **subordinate** to carry out the mundane chores. _____

8) It took several attempts to get the numbers to **tally**. _____

9) King Canute thought he could **stop** the advance of the tide. _____

10) Her mother left her a **substantial** inheritance. _____   Score ⬜ 10

Exercise 23b

11) The dessert was smothered with a **stodgy**, sickly sauce. _____

12) "Don't ever do that again!" he said **sternly**. "Now go to your room!" _____

13) The experiment was a total success and delivered **surprising** results. _____

14) The church's **stumpy** tower seems in keeping with its short nave. _____

15) She delivered a(n) **stimulating** lecture that captivated her audience. _____

16) His brother's camera is a **superior** model with many more features. _____

17) The family met at the crematorium to **strew** her grandfather's ashes. _____

18) He looked a mess dressed in a **sullied** suit and scuffed shoes. _____

19) It was **strange** that no-one claimed to have been there. _____   Score

20) The scratch was **superficial** and easily polished out. _____   ⬜ 10

Synonyms Word List

abandon	awkward	clockwise	dull
abode	backward	close	durable
absence	bad	cold	dwindle
abundant	baffle	come	eager
accept	banal	comfort	early
accord	barren	commemorate	ebb
accused	beautiful	common	eccentric
acute	beginning	competent	economise
admit	bend	conceal	educated
advance	berate	conceive	elaborate
advantage	best	confirmation	elude
adversity	betrayal	contradict	embezzle
affectionate	better	contribution	eminent
affluent	bias	correct	empty
aggravate	big	courage	encourage
agree	bitter	courteous	end
aid	blend	craving	endure
alike	bless	credulous	enemy
alive	bliss	cruel	entrance
alleviate	blunt	cunning	essential
ally	bold	dainty	estimate
always	bonus	damp	evaluate
amenable	brief	dare	excited
ancestor	bright	dark	exhaust
ancient	brilliant	decay	exhilarated
anguish	brisk	deceive	expensive
answer	budget	decent	explicit
apathetic	build	decrease	export
approach	buy	deep	exterior
approval	candid	definite	fail
arrival	captivity	demand	fall
arrogant	caricature	dense	famous
artificial	casual	despair	fast
ascend	category	detain	fastidious
asleep	caution	dirty	fat
assemble	cease	disaster	fatigue
astonishing	cellar	disclose	federation
asunder	chaotic	discourage	feeble
atrocious	cheap	disease	fervour
attack	cherish	dismal	feud
attention	circular	divide	few
attractive	circumvent	doctor	filth
augment	clear	dogma	find
avoid	clever	dry	first

48

Synonyms Word List

flatter	hasten	isolate	mariner
fleet	hasty	join	master
fold	hate	jovial	match
foolish	haughty	judge	mature
forget	healthy	junior	maze
fortunate	height	justice	meagre
found	here	justification	meditate
frank	hero	juvenile	memorial
freedom	hill	keen	mention
frequent	hinder	king	merge
friend	home	lament	merry
frivolous	honest	land	minority
frugal	horizontal	landlord	miser
full	humble	large	misunderstand
furious	humiliate	last	mute
gap	hunger	laugh	myth
gather	hygiene	lawful	nature
generous	hypocrisy	lawyer	near
gentle	ideal	lazy	neat
genuine	idle	lead	necessary
giant	illogical	leader	negate
glad	illustrious	lean	negligent
glare	imitate	leave	negotiate
gloomy	imitation	lecturer	new
goad	immense	lender	nice
granted	impartial	liberal	night
grasp	impatient	like	nimble
gravely	implicate	likely	noble
great	importune	limit	noisy
greed	imprison	limitation	North
grope	inadvertent	little	novice
guarantee	include	lofty	nuisance
guardian	increase	long	obedient
guile	indifferent	loss	objection
guilty	inferior	loud	obligatory
gullible	inhabited	low	observe
habitual	inhale	loyal	obvious
halt	inside	lucid	odd
handicap	insolent	lucky	offer
happy	intelligent	mad	omen
hard	intentional	malady	omit
harmful	interesting	manage	open
harmless	interior	manipulate	opportune
harsh	internal	marginal	optimist

Synonyms Word List

option	prudent	sense	tendency
out	puny	serious	term
pacify	pure	settle	thick
pain	qualified	shallow	thrift
paramount	queer	shopkeeper	thrust
partisan	radiate	shrewd	top
passive	ramble	significant	tough
past	rank	sleek	tranquil
parent	realize	slight	transfer
pause	recalcitrant	slim	transparent
peace	receptacle	smart	truth
permanent	reconcile	solid	tumult
permeate	reconciliation	sorrow	turbulent
perpetuate	regret	sow	upbeat
perplex	regularly	spontaneous	vacant
persuade	reliable	stabilize	vain
please	remedy	stern	valid
plentiful	reveal	straight	verify
polite	right	strong	victory
possible	rigid	success	virtue
poverty	rough	sunny	visible
powerful	sanction	suspended	wax
presence	satisfactory	take	wisdom
pretty	scatter	tall	withdraw
private	scope	tame	within
prohibit	section	tangle	wrath
prompt	security	temper	wretched

Congratulations!

You have now learnt **460** synonyms; know what they mean and how to use them in a sentence.

Now move on to the **Antonyms Book** to learn lots more words to add to your word bank total.

Answers

Exercise 1a

1) plentiful
2) success
3) genuine
4) implicate
5) leave
6) competent
7) bitter
8) juvenile
9) hasty
10) possible

Exercise 1b

11) admit
12) satisfactory
13) peace
14) dwindle
15) augment
16) pain
17) eccentric
18) realize
19) mature
20) inadvertent

Exercise 2a

1) open
2) nuisance
3) furious
4) tough
5) pacify
6) asunder
7) federation
8) disclose
9) nimble
10) attractive

Exercise 2b

11) budget
12) accord
13) atrocious
14) impatient
15) aggravate
16) height
17) amenable
18) indifferent
19) wrath
20) alive

Exercise 3a

1) attention
2) feud
3) presence
4) empty
5) come
6) verify
7) evaluate
8) lucky
9) greed
10) stern

Exercise 3b

11) haughty
12) out
13) negotiate
14) sanction
15) neat
16) attack
17) stabilize
18) circumvent
19) guarantee
20) valid

Crossword No. 1

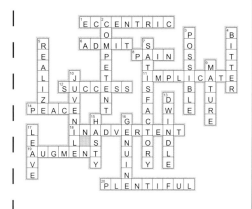

Letter = I

Crossword No. 2

Letter = R

Crossword No. 3

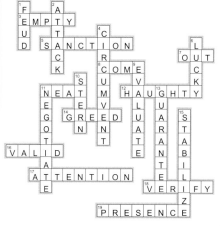

Letter = O

Answers

Exercise 4a

1) advantage
2) early
3) accused
4) limitation
5) dull
6) disaster
7) cellar
8) dogma
9) vain
10) novice

Exercise 4b

11) importune
12) master
13) intelligent
14) marginal
15) pretty
16) offer
17) bend
18) noisy
19) partisan
20) merge

Exercise 5a

1) internal
2) caution
3) deceive
4) option
5) lucid
6) upbeat
7) negligent
8) category
9) merry
10) hygiene

Exercise 5b

11) commemorate
12) hero
13) polite
14) memorial
15) gloomy
16) pure
17) dare
18) paramount
19) laugh
20) cold

Exercise 6a

1) agree
2) banal
3) obligatory
4) rough
5) imprison
6) flatter
7) brilliant
8) obedient
9) brief
10) transparent

Exercise 6b

11) include
12) giant
13) private
14) ascend
15) accept
16) persuade
17) end
18) friend
19) blend
20) gather

Crossword No. 4

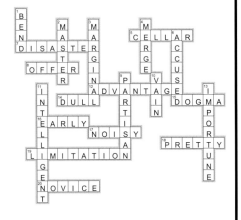

Letter = O

Crossword No. 5

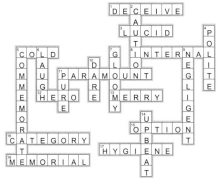

Letter = P

Crossword No. 6

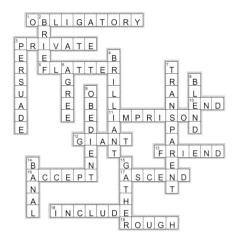

Letter = S

Answers

Exercise 7a
1) limit
2) remedy
3) thrift
4) berate
5) right
6) baffle
7) imitate
8) hunger
9) obvious
10) transfer

Exercise 7b
11) maze
12) receptacle
13) gullible
14) victory
15) expensive
16) manipulate
17) regularly
18) lender
19) negate
20) perpetuate

Exercise 8a
1) decay
2) essential
3) slight
4) guardian
5) harmful
6) granted
7) solid
8) guilty
9) term
10) bright

Exercise 8b
11) educated
12) intentional
13) bold
14) glad
15) loss
16) guile
17) night
18) habitual
19) smart
20) explicit

Exercise 9a
1) isolate
2) contradict
3) find
4) apathetic
5) hate
6) reliable
7) cease
8) abandon
9) lead
10) chaotic

Exercise 9b
11) exhaust
12) handicap
13) filth
14) conceive
15) captivity
16) barren
17) malady
18) craving
19) arrogant
20) adversity

Crossword No. 7

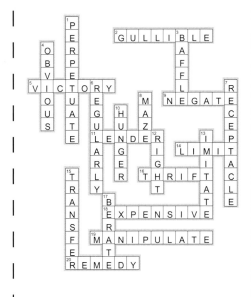

Letter = E

Crossword No. 8

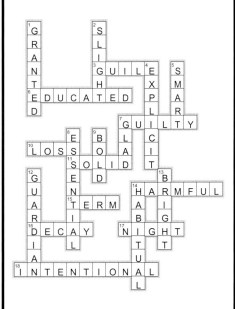

Letter = P

Crossword No. 9

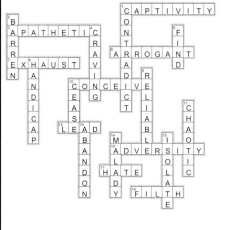

Letter = G

Answers

Exercise 10a

1) contribution
2) cheap
3) betrayal
4) anguish
5) nature
6) land
7) tame
8) mute
9) comfort
10) discourage

Exercise 10b

11) abode
12) section
13) hypocrisy
14) eager
15) clear
16) keen
17) entrance
18) eminent
19) fall
20) blunt

Exercise 11a

1) visible
2) build
3) necessary
4) bad
5) omit
6) radiate
7) vacant
8) judge
9) qualified
10) great

Exercise 11b

11) exhilarated
12) fastidious
13) elude
14) fatigue
15) cherish
16) permanent
17) wax
18) like
19) illustrious
20) elaborate

Exercise 12a

1) opportune
2) imitation
3) rank
4) justice
5) hard
6) last
7) definite
8) grope
9) sunny
10) brisk

Exercise 12b

11) healthy
12) full
13) best
14) parent
15) justification
16) truth
17) bonus
18) long
19) myth
20) loyal

Crossword No. 10

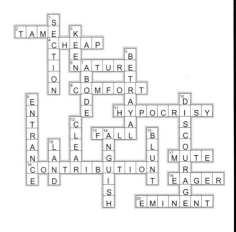

Letter = R

Crossword No. 11

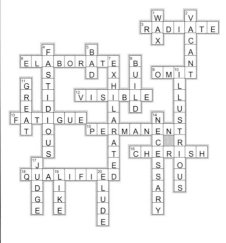

Letter = U

Crossword No. 12

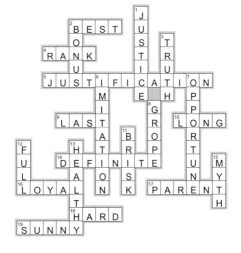

Letter = N

Answers

Exercise 13a

1) awkward
2) prohibit
3) dense
4) assemble
5) dark
6) frank
7) horizontal
8) grasp
9) please
10) ancestor

Exercise 13b

11) jovial
12) feeble
13) enemy
14) beautiful
15) common
16) glare
17) mad
18) always
19) inhale
20) dainty

Crossword No. 13

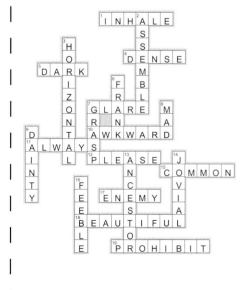

Letter = S

Exercise 14a

1) straight
2) sorrow
3) poverty
4) top
5) humiliate
6) past
7) estimate
8) immense
9) aid
10) decent

Exercise 14b

11) miser
12) lament
13) hinder
14) lofty
15) detain
16) candid
17) increase
18) bliss
19) credulous
20) gap

Crossword No. 14

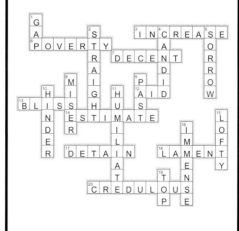

Letter = O

Exercise 15a

1) first
2) illogical
3) spontaneous
4) within
5) frivolous
6) suspended
7) harmless
8) idle
9) casual
10) optimist

Exercise 15b

11) tendency
12) rigid
13) asleep
14) alike
15) avoid
16) passive
17) serious
18) interior
19) lazy
20) artificial

Crossword No. 15

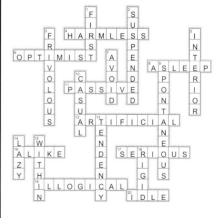

Letter = E

Answers

Exercise 16a

1) fervour
2) bless
3) happy
4) demand
5) lawful
6) decrease
7) liberal
8) few
9) settle
10) slim

Exercise 16b

11) encourage
12) generous
13) endure
14) freedom
15) virtue
16) absence
17) inside
18) big
19) tangle
20) hill

Exercise 17a

1) king
2) humble
3) wretched
4) cruel
5) alleviate
6) temper
7) despair
8) powerful
9) nice
10) damp

Exercise 17b

11) misunderstand
12) noble
13) dismal
14) courage
15) gentle
16) tall
17) fortunate
18) approach
19) affectionate
20) caricature

Exercise 18a

1) fat
2) scope
3) close
4) strong
5) lawyer
6) fleet
7) objection
8) perplex
9) new
10) arrival

Exercise 18b

11) excited
12) observe
13) loud
14) ancient
15) home
16) fail
17) impartial
18) recalcitrant
19) near
20) significant

Crossword No. 16

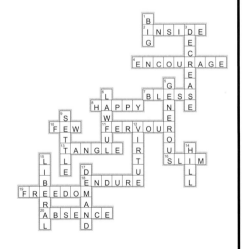

Crossword No. 17

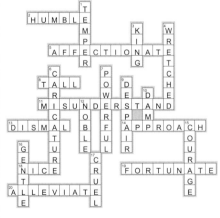

Crossword No. 18

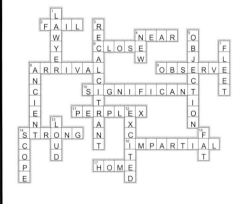

Letter = W

Letter = R

Letter = F

Answers

Exercise 19a

1) fold
2) tumult
3) leader
4) inhabited
5) shrewd
6) abundant
7) dry
8) tranquil
9) meditate
10) forget

Exercise 19b

11) queer
12) sense
13) courteous
14) North
15) ideal
16) ally
17) lecturer
18) doctor
19) affluent
20) exterior

Exercise 20a

1) likely
2) embezzle
3) prompt
4) confirmation
5) bias
6) sow
7) puny
8) landlord
9) here
10) fast

Exercise 20b

11) correct
12) deep
13) omen
14) approval
15) advance
16) goad
17) thrust
18) buy
19) frugal
20) wisdom

Exercise 21a

1) found
2) answer
3) ebb
4) regret
5) pause
6) famous
7) frequent
8) take
9) ramble
10) mariner

Exercise 21b

11) shopkeeper
12) hasten
13) circular
14) withdraw
15) manage
16) durable
17) backward
18) insolent
19) security
20) reconcile

Crossword No. 19

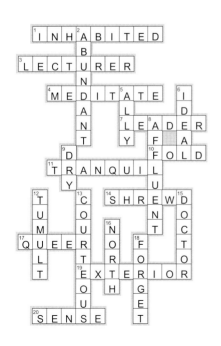

Letter = E

Crossword No. 20

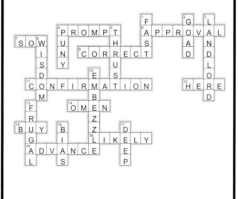

Letter = O

Crossword No. 21

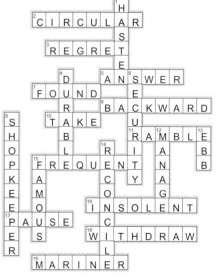

Letter = T

Answers

Exercise 22a

1) disease
2) reveal
3) prudent
4) clever
5) divide
6) little
7) permeate
8) clockwise
9) export
10) lean

Exercise 22b

11) economize
12) minority
13) acute
14) sleek
15) foolish
16) cunning
17) conceal
18) honest
19) reconciliation
20) meagre

Crossword No. 22

Letter = S

Exercise 23a

1) harsh
2) beginning
3) inferior
4) join
5) turbulent
6) mention
7) junior
8) match
9) halt
10) large

Exercise 23b

11) thick
12) gravely
13) astonishing
14) low
15) interesting
16) better
17) scatter
18) dirty
19) odd
20) shallow

Crossword No. 23

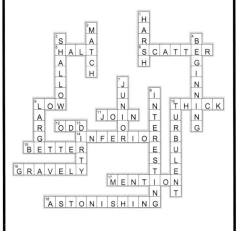

Letter = A

Mystery Word

I R O O P S E P
P O R P O I S E

Mystery Word

G R U N S O E
S U R G E O N

Mystery Word

W R F E O T S A
S O F T W A R E

PROGRESS CHARTS

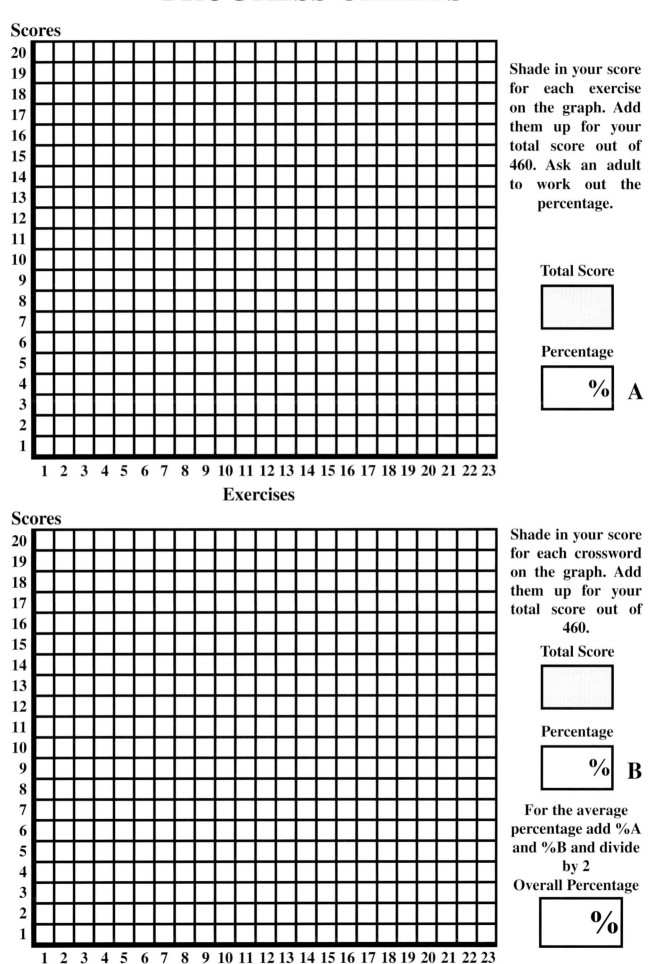

Scores

Exercises

Shade in your score for each exercise on the graph. Add them up for your total score out of 460. Ask an adult to work out the percentage.

Total Score

Percentage

% **A**

Scores

Crosswords

Shade in your score for each crossword on the graph. Add them up for your total score out of 460.

Total Score

Percentage

% **B**

For the average percentage add %A and %B and divide by 2

Overall Percentage

%

CERTIFICATE OF

ACHIEVEMENT

This certifies

_____

has successfully completed

11+ Semantics

WORKBOOK **1**

Overall percentage
score achieved

%

Comment _____

_____

Signed _____
(teacher/parent/guardian)

Date _____